I Dreamed A

SUSAN

BOYLE

Published by
Wise Publications
14-15 Berners Street, London W1T 3LJ, UK.

Exclusive Distributors:
Music Sales Limited
Distribution Centre, Newmarket Road,
Bury St Edmunds, Suffolk IP33 3YB, UK.

Music Sales Pty Limited
20 Resolution Drive, Caringbah,
NSW 2229, Australia.

Order No. AM999383
ISBN 978-1-84938-377-6

Edited by Jenni Wheeler.

Arrangements by Christopher Hussey, Jeremy Birchall,
Mark Lloyd & Simon Townley

www.musicsales.com

Printed in the EU.

I Dreamed A Dream

SUSAN
BOYLE

WISE PUBLICATIONS
part of The Music Sales Group
London/New York/Paris/Sydney/Copenhagen/Berlin/Tokyo/Madrid

Wild Horses

Words & Music by Mick Jagger & Keith Richards

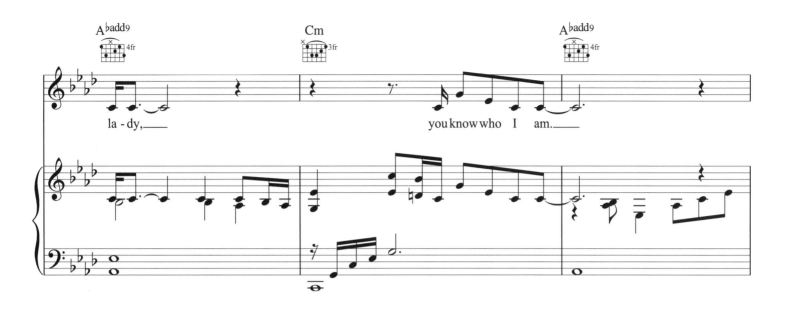

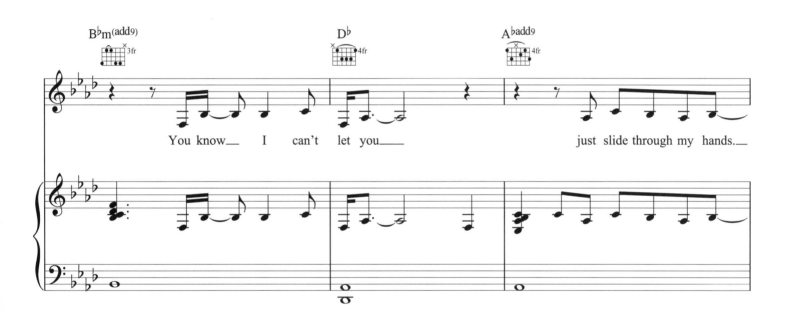

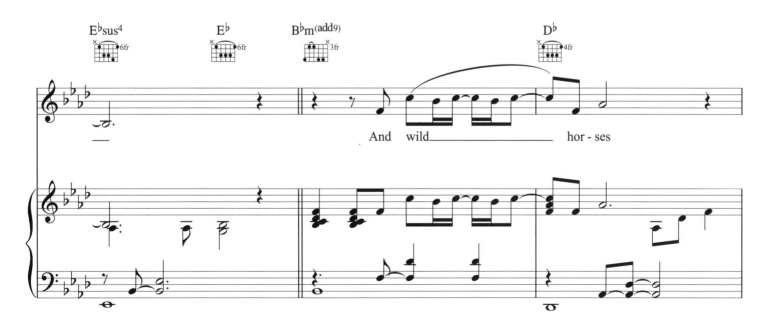

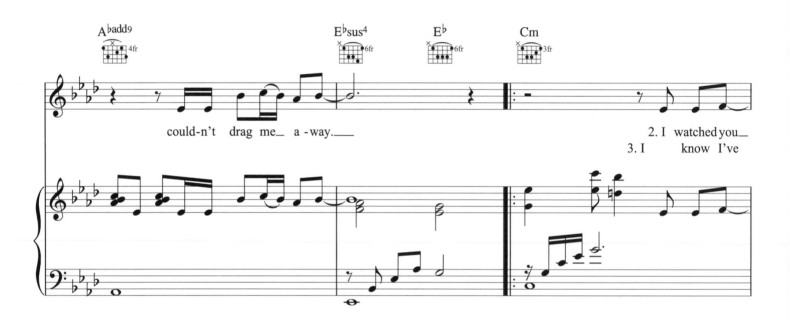

and now you've de - ci - ded
and I have my____ free-dom,

to show__ me__ the same.__
but I don't have__ much time.__

No sweep-ing ex - its____
Fate has been suf - fered____

or____ off - stage lines____
and tears__ must__ be cried;

could make me feel__
so let's do some

9

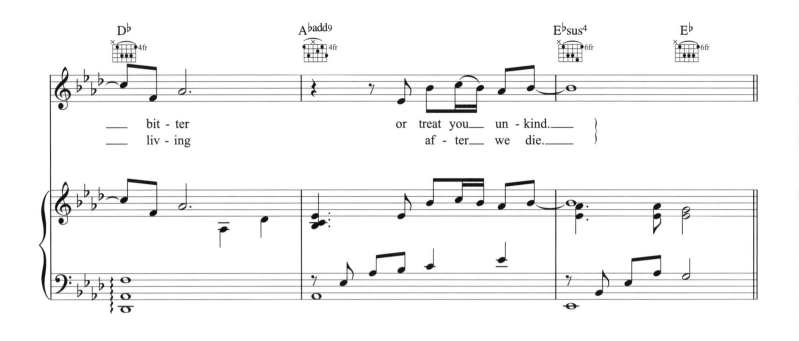

__ bit - ter   or treat you__ un - kind.__
__ liv - ing   af - ter__ we die.__

And wild_____ hor - ses__   could-n't drag me_ a - way,

1.

and wild_____ hor - ses

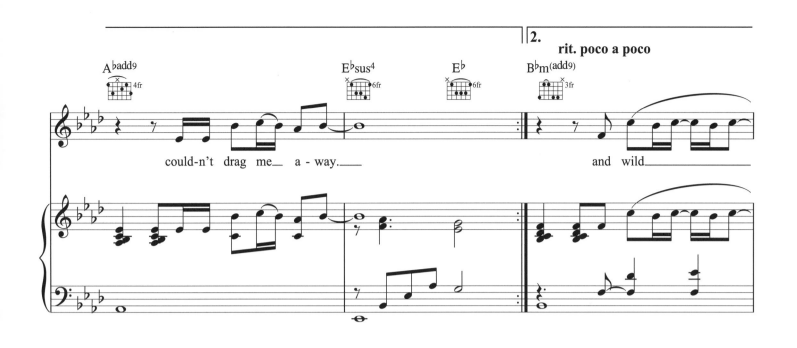

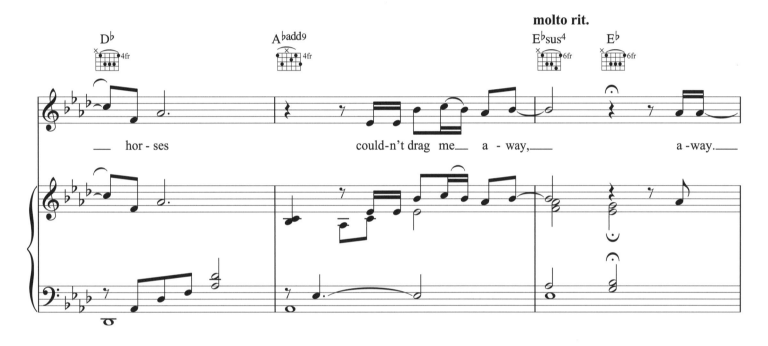

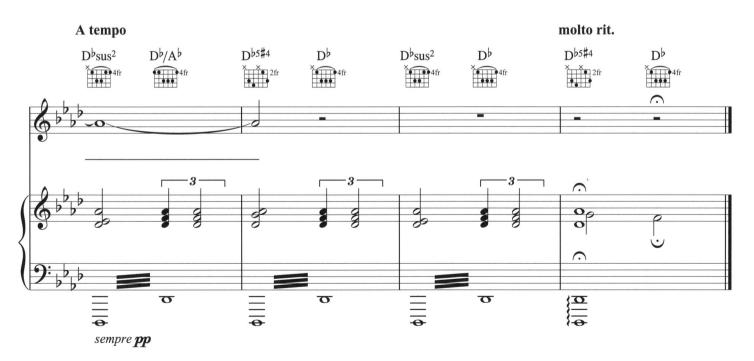

I Dreamed A Dream

Music by Claude-Michel Schönberg
Original Lyrics by Alain Boublil & Jean-Marc Natel
English Lyrics by Herbert Kretzmer

no song un - sung,__ no wine__ un - tas - ted.____

More movement

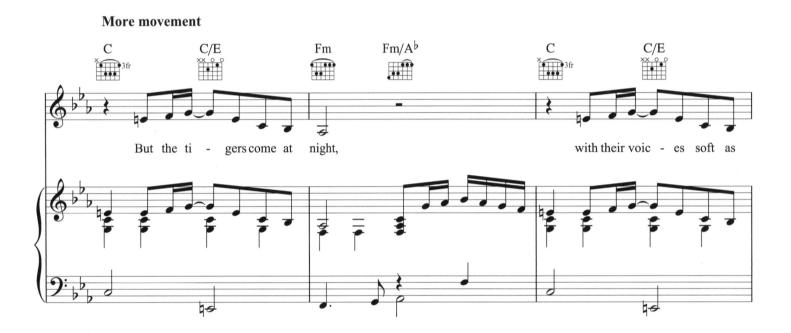

But the ti - gers come at night, with their voic - es soft as

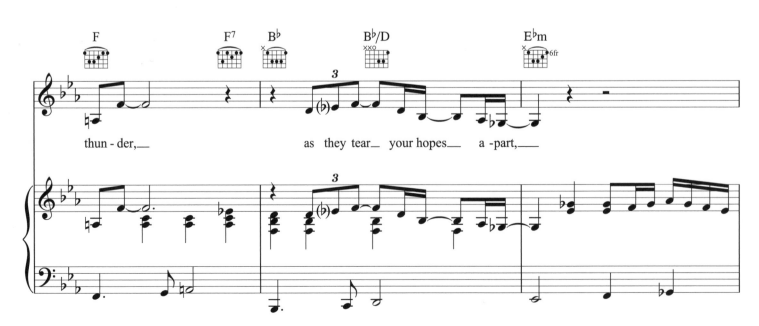

thun - der,__ as they tear_ your hopes_ a -part,__

and they turn your dream to shame.

Broadly

Still I dream he'll come to me,

that we will live the years to geth - er;

15

but there are dreams____ that can - not be,_____

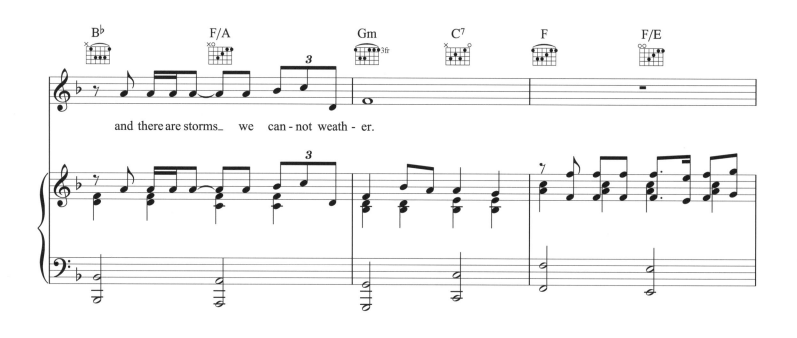

and there are storms_ we can - not weath - er.

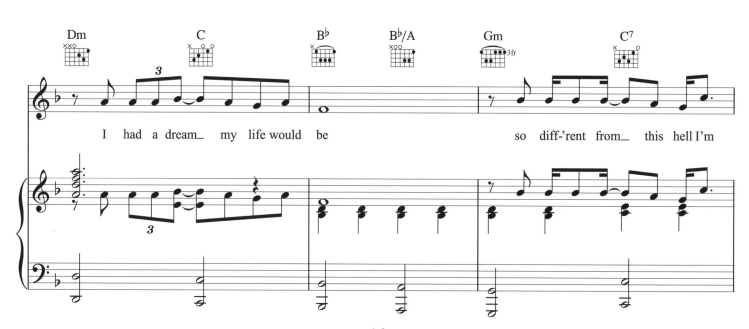

I had a dream_ my life would be   so diff-'rent from_ this hell I'm

liv - ing, so diff -'rent now from what it seemed,___

Slower

now life has killed___ the dream___ I dreamed.

rit. poco a poco

Cry Me A River

Words & Music by Arthur Hamilton

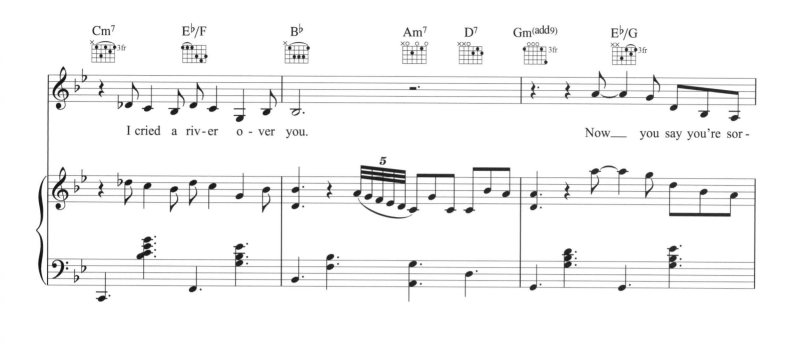

I cried a riv-er o-ver you. Now___ you say you're sor-

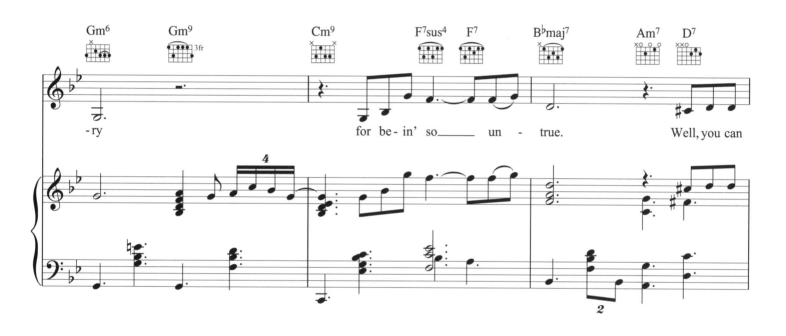

-ry for be-in' so___ un - true. Well, you can

cry___ me a riv-er,___ cry me a riv-er;___ I cried a riv-er o-ver

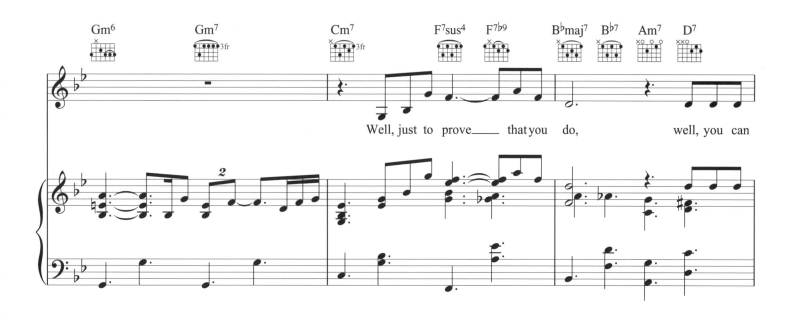

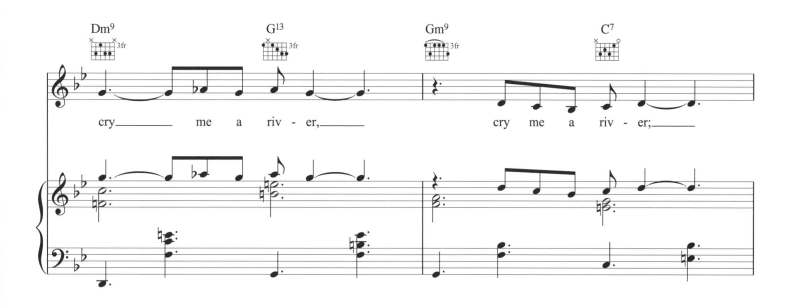

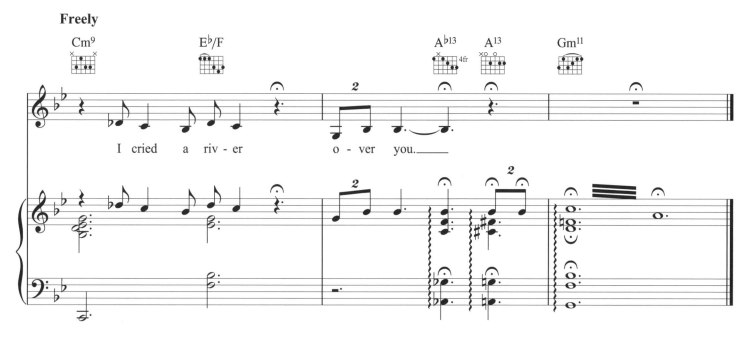

How Great Thou Art

Traditional

how great Thou art! How great Thou art! Then sings my

Then sings my soul, my Sav - iour God, to Thee,

how great Thou art! How great Thou art! Then sings my

soul, my Sav - iour God, to Thee, how great Thou

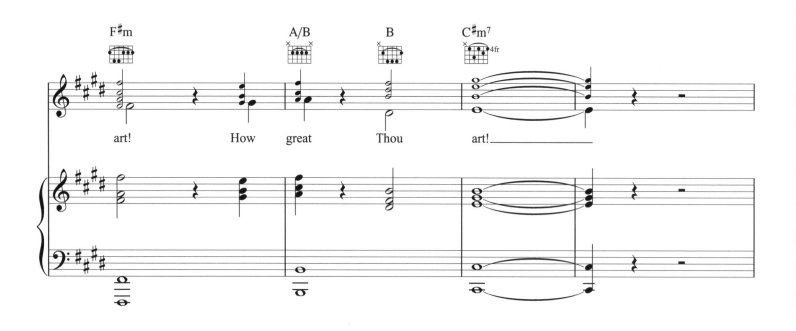

art! How great Thou art!_____

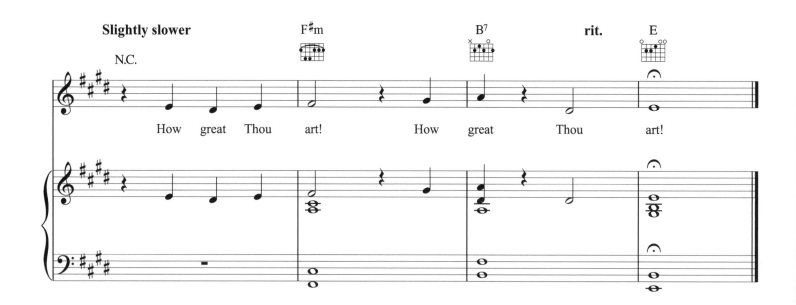

How great Thou art! How great Thou art!

Up To The Mountain

Words & Music by Patricia Griffin

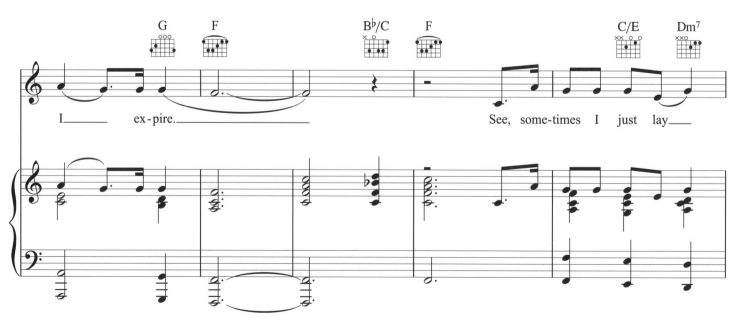

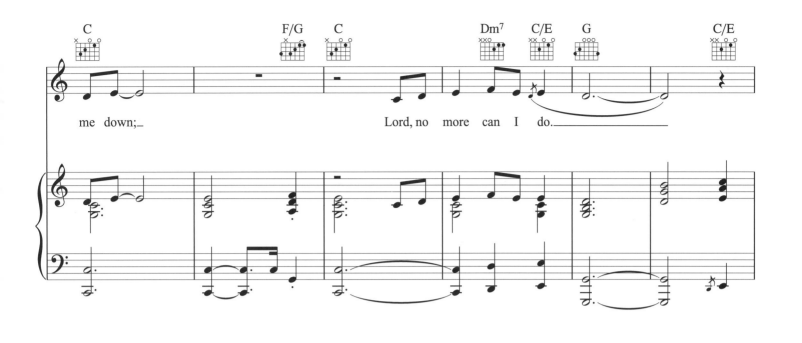

me down;____   Lord, no more can I do._____

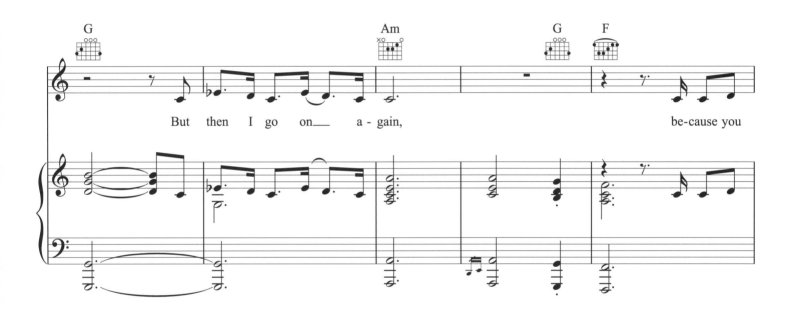

But then I go on____ a - gain,   be-cause you

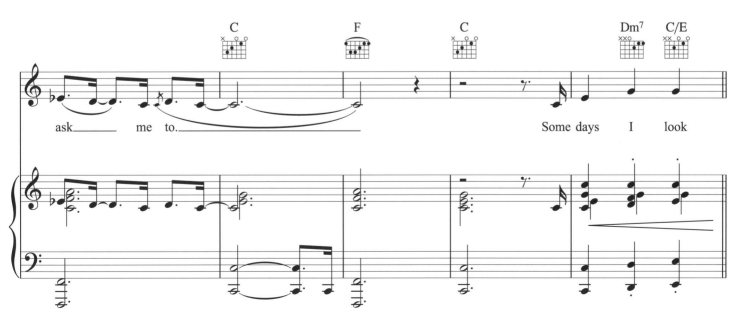

ask____ me to._____   Some days I look

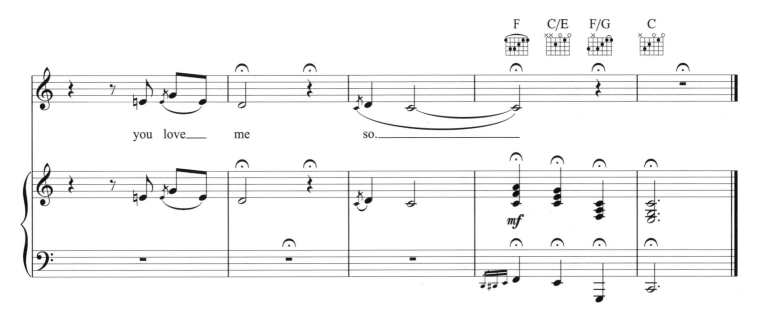

You'll See

Words & Music by Madonna & David Foster

You think___ I have noth-ing___ with-out___ you___ by___
You think___ af-ter all___ you've done, I'll nev-er find___ my___ way___

1.

___ my side;___ you'll see,___ some-how,___ some - day.___
___ back home;___

2.

2. You   you'll see,___ some - how,___ some - day.___

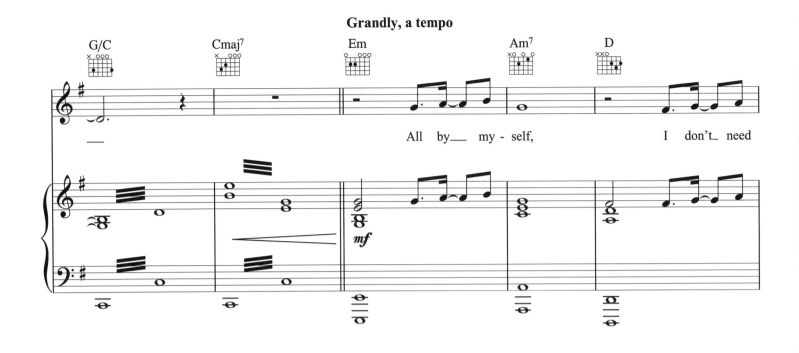

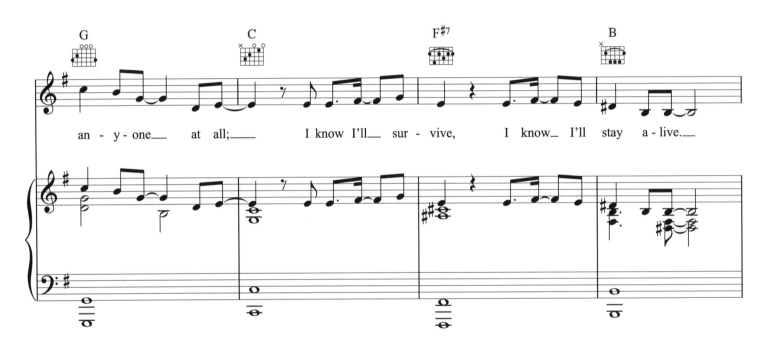

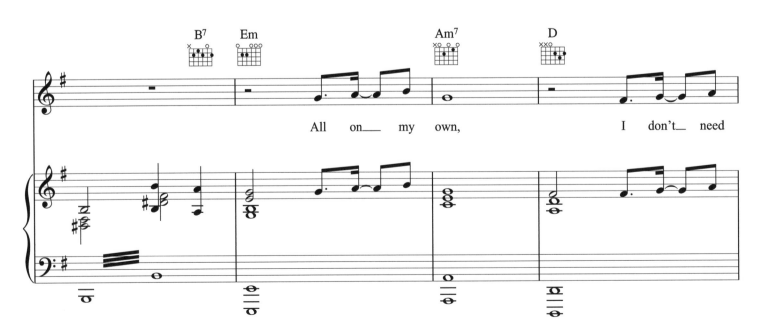

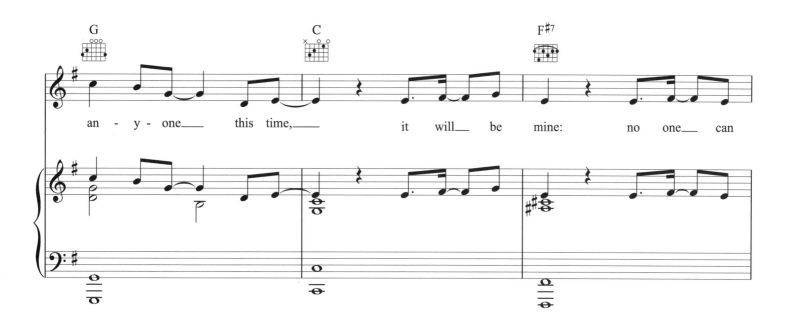

an - y - one___ this time,___ it will__ be mine: no one__ can

More rhythmically

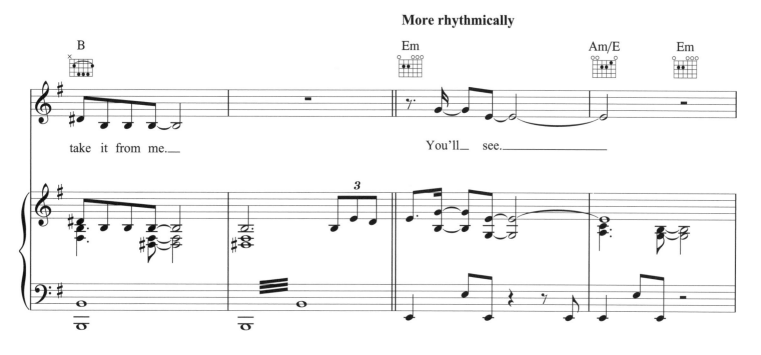

take it from me.__ You'll__ see._____

3. You think that you__ are strong,__ but you are weak;__

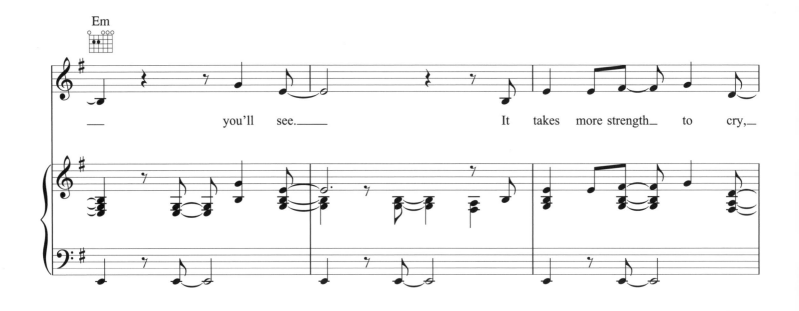

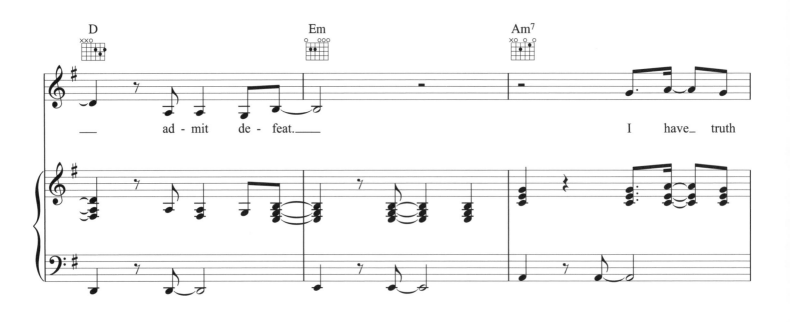

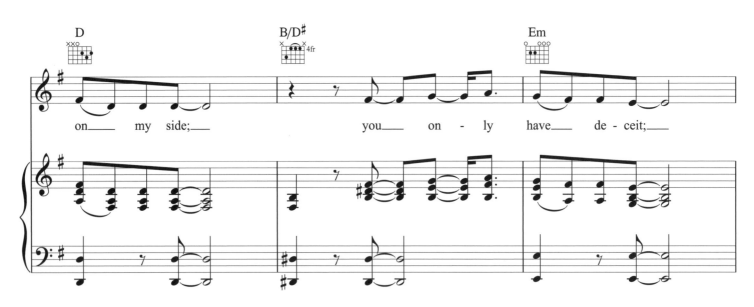

you'll see,___ some-how,___ some - day.___

All by___ my - self,

I don't__ need an - y-one___ at all;___ I know I'll__ sur -

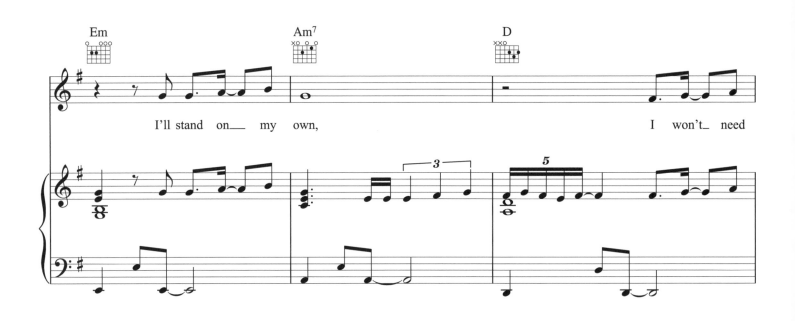

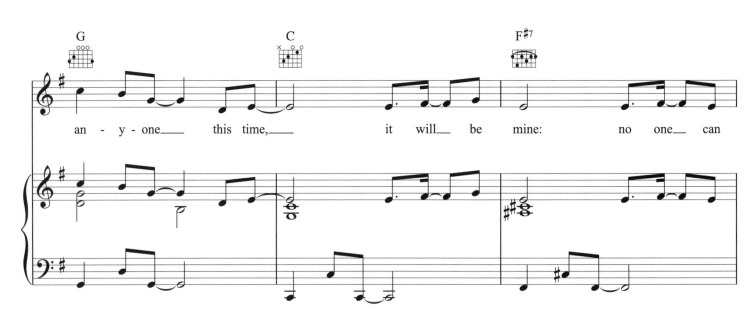

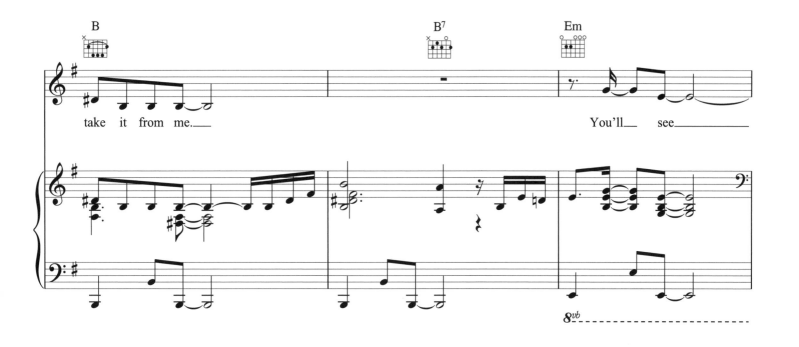

take it from me._____   You'll___ see_____

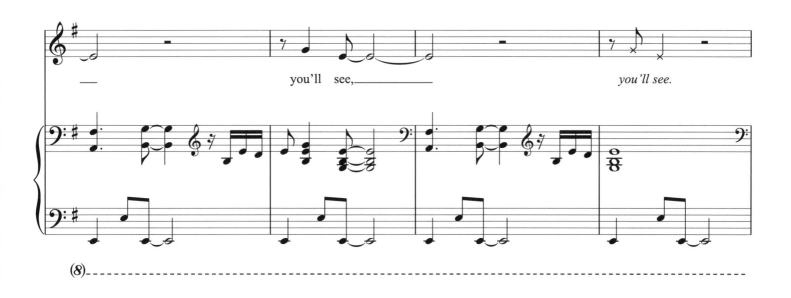

____   you'll see,_____   *you'll see.*

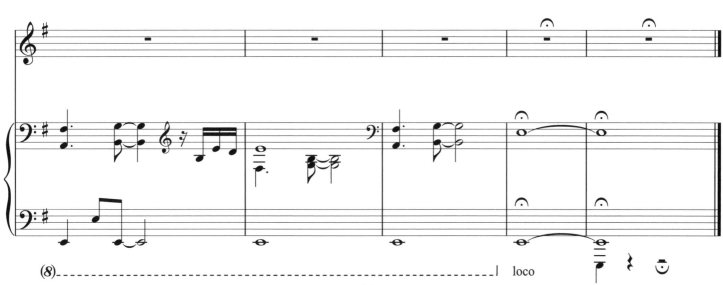

loco

Daydream Believer

Words & Music by John Stewart

wipe the sleep out___ of___ my eyes;_____ the

tears of yes - ter - day___ don't mean a thing._____

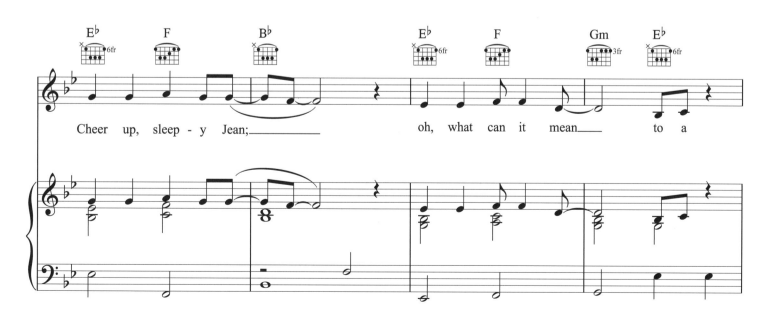

Cheer up, sleep - y Jean;_____ oh, what can it mean___ to a

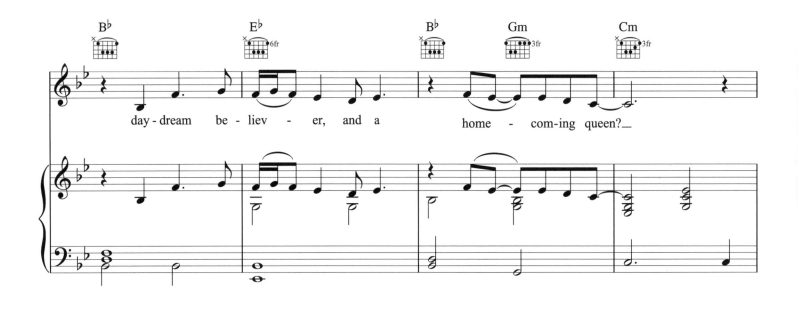

day-dream be - liev - er, and a   home - com-ing queen?

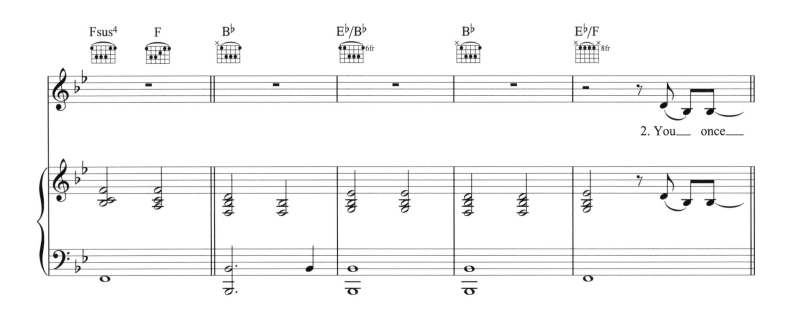

2. You___ once___

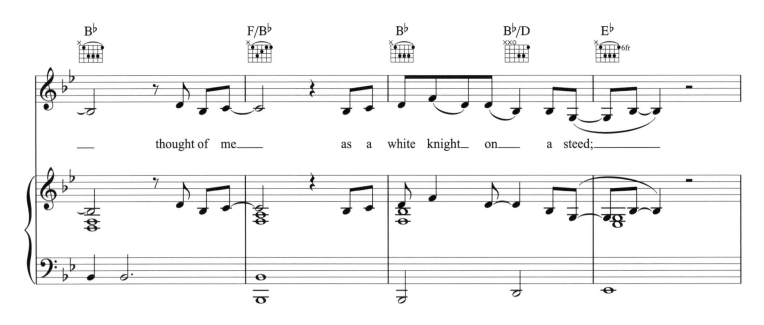

thought of me___   as a white knight___ on___ a steed;___

42

now you know__ how__ hap - py__ I can be. And our__

good times__ start and end with-out dol - lar,__ one__ to spend,__ but

how much, ba - by, do__ we real - ly need?__

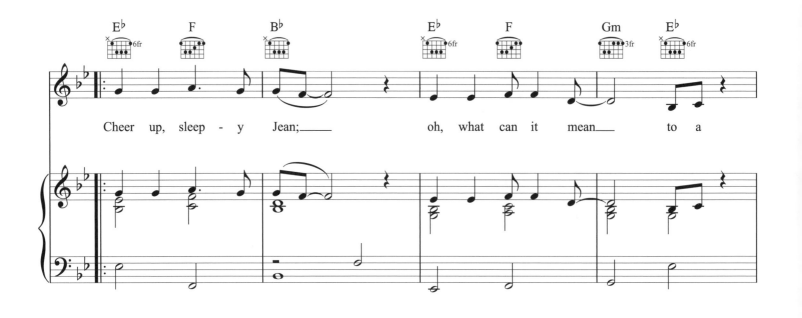

Cheer up, sleep - y Jean;____ oh, what can it mean____ to a

day - dream be - liev - er, and a home - com - ing queen?____

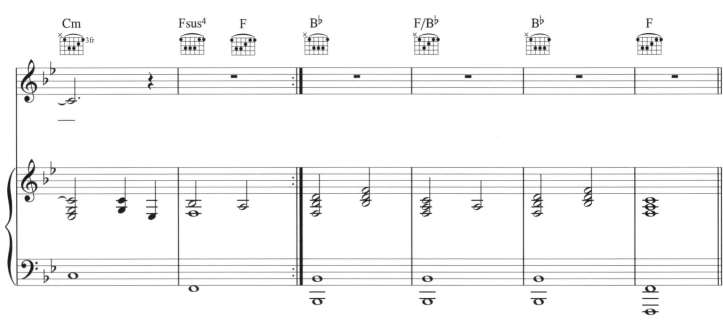

44

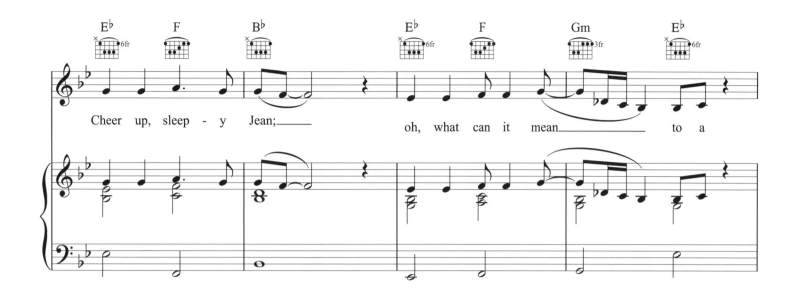

Cheer up, sleep - y Jean;____ oh, what can it mean_____ to a

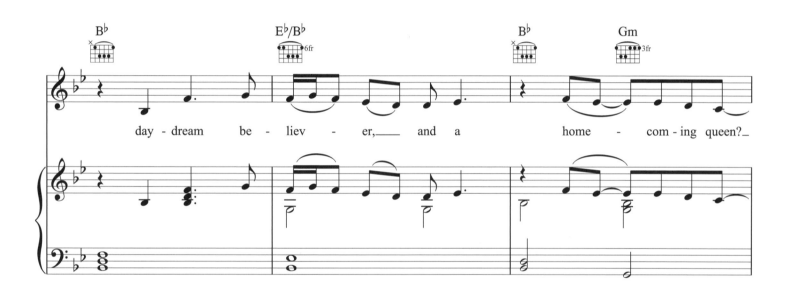

day - dream be - liev - er,____ and a home - com - ing queen?_

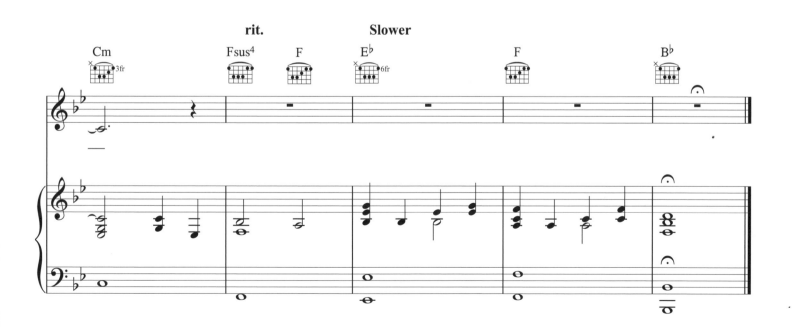

rit.   Slower

Amazing Grace

Traditional

Arranged by Steve Mac, Carlos Marin, Urs Buhler,
Sebastian Izambard, David Arch & David Miller

days   to   sing   God's   praise   than____   when   we've____

D.S. al Coda   **⊕ Coda**

first   be -   gun._____   4. A -   see,

Freely

N.C.

was   blind,   but_____   now   I   see.

Who I Was Born To Be

Words & Music by Audra Butts, Johan Fransson,
Tobias Lundgren & Tim Larsson

all   come a-round   a - gain.

And though I may_____ not____ know_ the

an - - swers,_ I can fi - n'ly say I'm free.

And if the ques - - tions___ led me

D.S. al Coda

p 3. When

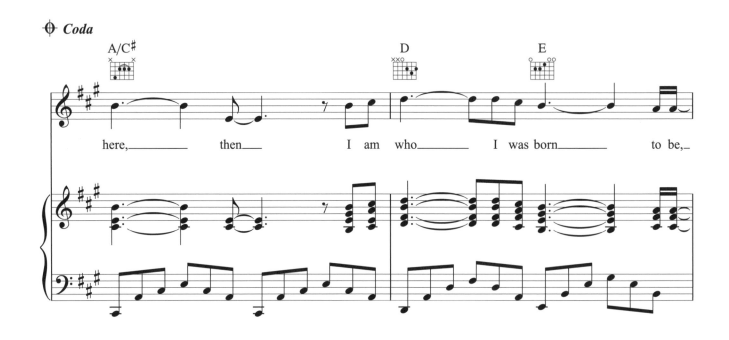

here,_____ then_____ I am who_____ I was born_____ to be,_

molto rit.   Freely, slower

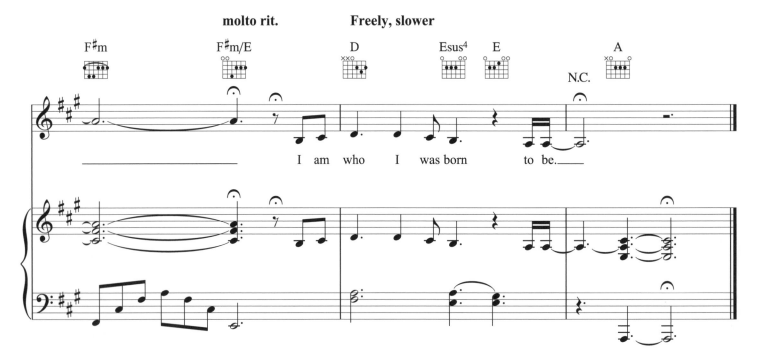

I am who I was born to be._____

The End Of The World

Words by Sylvia Dee
Music by Arthur Kent

Original key: B major

Innocently ♩. = 52

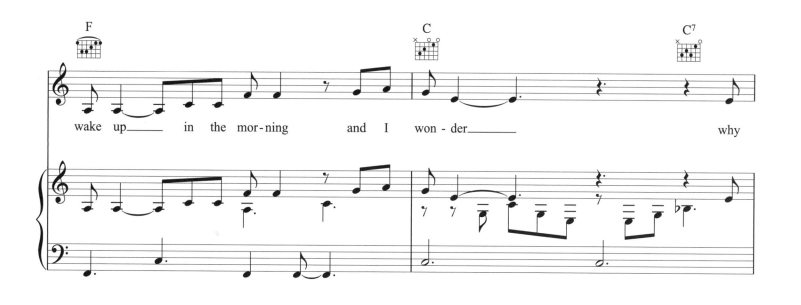

wake up_____ in the mor-ning and I won-der_____ why

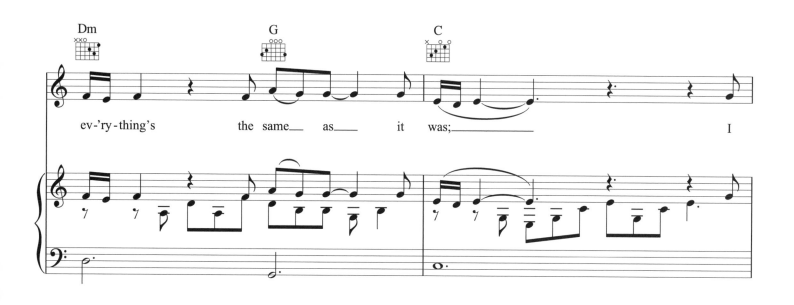

ev-'ry-thing's the same___ as___ it was;_____ I

can't_____ un-der-stand, no I can't_____ un-der-stand how

life   goes   on   the way it does.

3. Why_____ does my heart   go on beat-ing?_____   Why_____ do these eyes of____ mine

cry?   Don't   they   know_____ it's the end_____ of the world?   It

end - ed___ when you said   good - bye.___

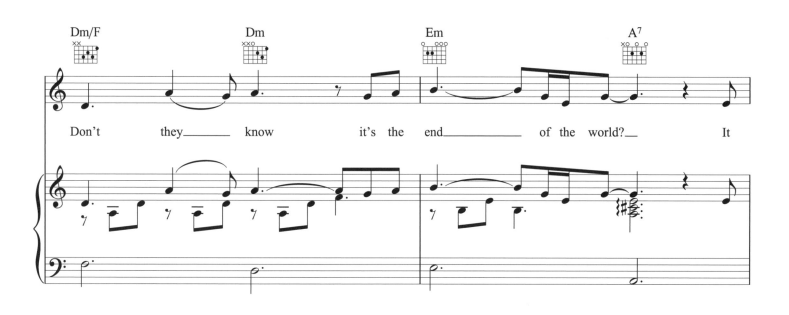

Don't   they___ know   it's the   end_____ of the world?___   It

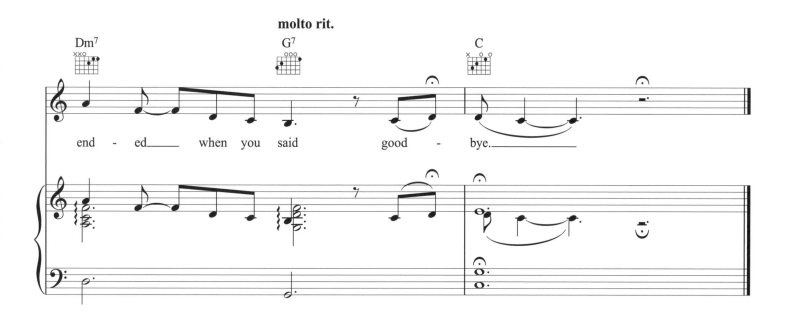

end - ed___   when you said   good - bye._____

Proud

Words & Music by Wayne Hector, Andy Hill & Steve Mac

63

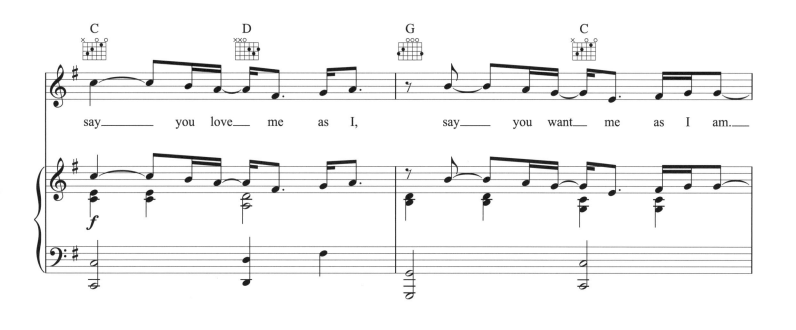

say_____ you love_____ me as I, say_____ you want_____ me as I am.

_____ Say I'm some-one in your eyes;_____ that's all I want-ed to_____ be.

Oh, just let me go;_____ I know_____ one day, if I'm_____ al-lowed,_____

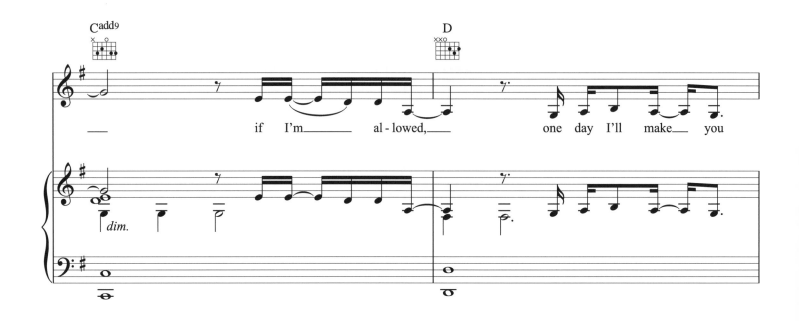

if I'm_____ al - lowed,_____ one day I'll make_____ you

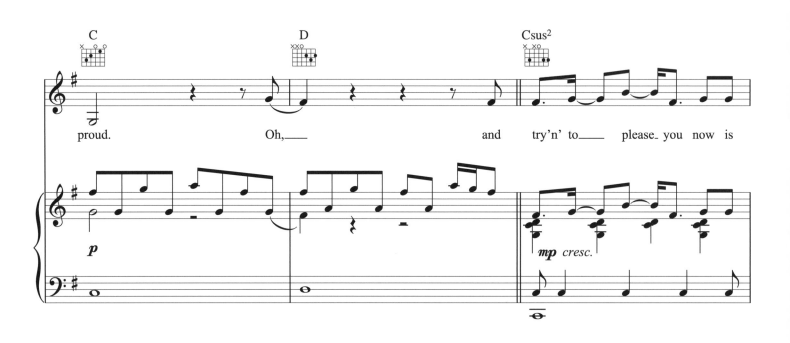

proud. Oh,_____ and try'n' to_____ please_ you now is

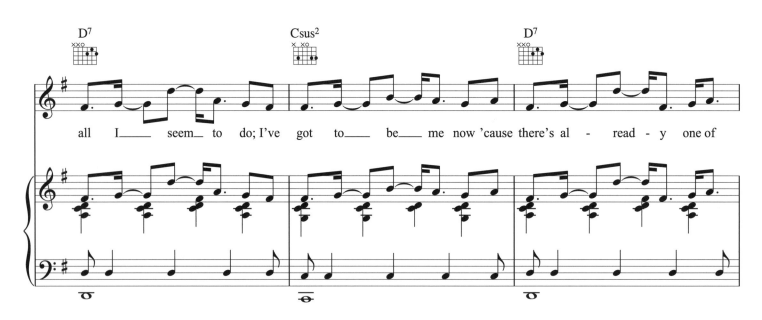

all I_____ seem_ to do; I've got to_____ be_ me now 'cause there's al - read - y one of

Silent Night

Words by Joseph Mohr
Music by Franz Gruber
Arranged by Steve Mac & David Arch

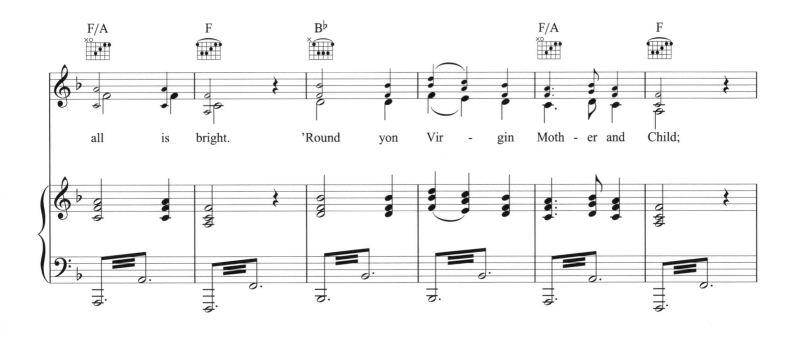

all is bright. 'Round yon Vir - gin Moth - er and Child;

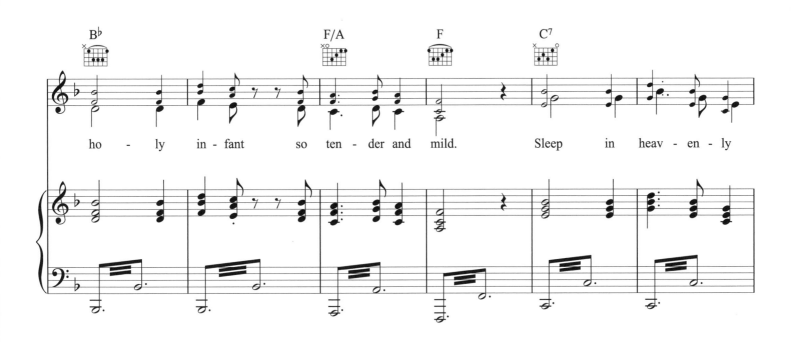

ho - ly in - fant so ten - der and mild. Sleep in heav - en - ly

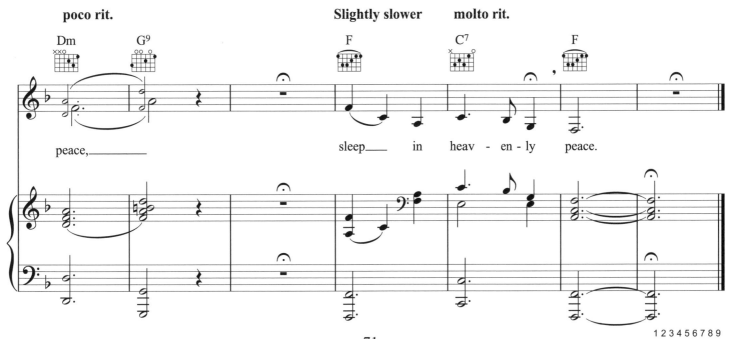

poco rit.   **Slightly slower**   **molto rit.**

peace,_____   sleep___ in heav - en - ly peace.

1 2 3 4 5 6 7 8 9